Professional Services Contract

This contract should be used for the appointment of a supplier to provide professional services

An NEC document

June 2005
(with amendments June 2006)

Construction Clients' Board endorsement of NEC3

The Construction Clients' Board (formerly Public Sector Construction Clients' Forum) recommends that public sector organisations use the NEC3 contracts when procuring construction. Standardising use of this comprehensive suite of contracts should help to deliver efficiencies across the public sector and promote behaviours in line with the principles of *Achieving Excellence in Construction*.

NEC is a division of Thomas Telford Ltd, which is a wholly owned subsidiary of the Institution of Civil Engineers (ICE), the owner and developer of the NEC.

The NEC is a family of standard contracts, each of which has these characteristics:

- Its use stimulates good management of the relationship between the two parties to the contract and, hence, of the work included in the contract.
- It can be used in a wide variety of commercial situations, for a wide variety of types of work and in any location.
- It is a clear and simple document – using language and a structure which are straightforward and easily understood.

NEC3 Professional Services Contract is one of the NEC family and is consistent with all other NEC3 documents. Also available are the Guidance Notes and Flow Charts.

ISBN (complete box set) 978 07277 3675 8
ISBN (this document) 978 07277 3370 2
ISBN (Guidance Notes and Flow Charts) 978 07277 3371 9

First edition 1994
Second edition 1998
Third edition June 2005
Reprinted with amendments 2006
Reprinted 2007, 2008, 2009, 2010 (thrice), 2011, 2012

Cover photo, Golden Jubilee Bridge, courtesy of City of Westminster

9 8 7 6

British Library Cataloguing in Publication Data for this publication is available from the British Library.

Typeset by Academic + Technical, Bristol

Printed and bound in Great Britain by Bell & Bain Limited, Glasgow, UK

CONTENTS

ACKNOWLEDGEMENTS

The first edition of the NEC Professional Services Contract was drafted by P. Higgins working on behalf of the Institution of Civil Engineers, with the assistance of F. Griffiths of the Chartered Institute of Purchasing and Supply and M. Coleman of the Association of Project Managers. Dr Martin Barnes then of Coopers and Lybrand advised on the co-ordination of the contract with the NEC.

The second edition of the NEC Professional Services Contract was mainly drafted by Bill Weddell with the assistance of Peter Higgins and Tom Nicholson as members of the NEC Panel with advice from Professor Phillip Capper then of Masons Solicitors.

The NEC Panel also had the benefit of comments of the Construction Industry Council's Task Force, which was established to investigate harmonisation of Conditions of Engagement (1994–95).

The third edition of the NEC Professional Services Contract was mainly drafted by Bill Weddell with the assistance of members of the NEC Panel. The Flow Charts were produced by Robert Gerrard with assistance from Ross Hayes and Tom Nicholson.

The original NEC was designed and drafted by Dr Martin Barnes then of Coopers and Lybrand with the assistance of Professor J. G. Perry then of the University of Birmingham, T. W. Weddell then of Travers Morgan Management, T. H. Nicholson, Consultant to the Institution of Civil Engineers, A. Norman then of the University of Manchester Institute of Science and Technology and P. A. Baird, then Corporate Contracts Consultant, Eskom, South Africa.

The members of the NEC Panel are:

    P. Higgins, BSc, CEng, FICE, FCIArb (Chairman)
    P. A. Baird, BSc, CEng, FICE, M(SA)ICE, MAPM
    M. Barnes, BSc(Eng), PhD, FREng, FICE, FCIOB, CCMI, ACIArb, MBCS, FInstCES, FAPM
    A. J. Bates, FRICS, MInstCES
    A. J. M. Blackler, BA, LLB(Cantab), MCIArb
    P. T. Cousins, BEng(Tech), DipArb, CEng, MICE, MCIArb, MCMI
    L. T. Eames, BSc, FRICS, FCIOB
    F. Forward, BA(Hons), DipArch, MSc(Const Law), RIBA, FCIArb
    Professor J. G. Perry, MEng, PhD, CEng, FICE, MAPM
    N. C. Shaw, FCIPS, CEng, MIMechE
    T. W. Weddell, BSc, CEng, DIC, FICE, FIStructE, ACIArb

NEC Consultant

    R. A. Gerrard, BSc(Hons), MRICS, FCIArb, FInstCES

Secretariat

    A. Cole, LLB, LLM, BL
    J. M. Hawkins, BA(Hons), MSc
    F. N. Vernon (Technical Adviser), BSc, CEng, MICE

SCHEDULE OF OPTIONS

The strategy for choosing the form of contract starts with a decision between four main Options, one of which must be chosen.

Option A	Priced contract with activity schedule
Option C	Target contract
Option E	Time based contract
Option G	Term contract
Note	Options B, D and F are not used

One of the following dispute resolution Options must be selected to complete the chosen main Option.

Option W1	Dispute resolution procedure (used unless United Kingdom Housing Grants, Construction and Regeneration Act 1996 applies).
Option W2	Dispute resolution procedure (used in the United Kingdom when the Housing Grants, Construction and Regeneration Act 1996 applies).

The following secondary Options should then be considered. It is not necessary to use any of them. Any combination other than those stated may be used.

Option X1	Price adjustment for inflation
Option X2	Changes in the law
Option X3	Multiple currencies (used only with Options A and G)
Option X4	Parent company guarantee
Option X5	Sectional Completion (not used with Option G)
Option X6	Bonus for early Completion (not used with Option G)
Option X7	Delay damages
Option X8	*Collateral warranty agreements*
Option X9	Transfer of rights
Option X10	*Employer's Agent*
Option X11	Termination by the *Employer*
Option X12	Partnering
Option X13	Performance bond
Option X18	Limitation of liability
Option X20	Key Performance Indicators (not used with Option X12)
Option Y	The following Options dealing with national legislation should be included if required.
Option Y(UK)2	The Housing Grants, Construction and Regeneration Act 1996
Option Y(UK)3	The Contracts (Rights of Third Parties) Act 1999
Option Z	*Additional conditions of contract*
Note	Options X14 to X17, X19 and Y(UK)1 are not used.

AMENDMENTS JUNE 2006

The following amendments have been made to the June 2005 edition.

Page	Clause	Line	
10	32.1	4	deleted: 'and of notified early warning matters'
17	70.4	2	'otherwise' inserted after 'stated'
23	50.4	1	'of Time Charge made by the *Consultant*' replaced by 'for staff whose *staff rate* is stated in the Contract Data'
		3	'him' replaced by 'the *Consultant*'
25	50.4	1	'50.4' replaced by '50.5'
	50.5	1	'of Time Charge made by the *Consultant*' replaced by 'for staff whose *staff rate* is stated in the Contract Data'
		3	deleted 'Such payments are converted to the *currency of this contract* in order to calculate the *Consultant*'s share using the *exchange rates*'
		3	'him' replaced by 'the *Consultant*'
26	50.4	1	'50.4' replaced by '50.6'
	50.6	1	'Payments of Time Charge made by the *Consultant*' replaced by 'Payments for • staff whose *staff rate* in the Contract Data or • items whose prices in the Task Schedule are stated'
		3	'him' replaced by 'the *Consultant*'
		3	deleted 'Such payments are converted to the *currency of this contract* in order to calculate the *Consultant*'s share using the *exchange rates*'
42	Contract Data Part one, 1.	3	added, '(with amendments June 2006)'
43	Contract Data Part one, 3.	1	'• The *Consultant* submits revised programmes at intervals no longer than . . . . . weeks' inserted after '• The *starting date* is . . . . .'
50	Contract Data Part two.		'If Option A or C is used •The tendered total of the Prices is . . . .' is inserted at the end of the Contract Data

www.neccontracts.com

nec®3 Professional Services Contract

CORE CLAUSES

1 General

Actions **10**

10.1 The *Employer* and the *Consultant* shall act as stated in this contract and in a spirit of mutual trust and co-operation.

Identified and defined **11**
terms 11.1 In these conditions of contract, terms identified in the Contract Data are in italics and defined terms have capital initials.

11.2 (1) The Accepted Programme is the programme identified in the Contract Data or is the latest programme accepted by the *Employer*. The latest programme accepted by the *Employer* supersedes previous Accepted Programmes.

(2) Completion is when the *Consultant* has

- done all the work which the Scope states he is to do by the Completion Date and
- corrected Defects which would have prevented the *Employer* from using the *services* and Others from doing their work.

If the work which the *Consultant* is to do by the Completion Date is not stated in the Scope, Completion is when the *Consultant* has done all the work necessary for the *Employer* to use the *services* and for Others to do their work.

(3) The Completion Date is the *completion date* unless later changed in accordance with this contract.

(4) The Contract Date is the date when this contract came into existence.

(5) A Defect is a part of the *services* which is not in accordance with the Scope or the applicable law.

(6) A Key Date is the date by which work is to meet the Condition stated. The Key Date is the *key date* stated in the Contract Data and the Condition is the *condition* stated in the Contract Data unless later changed in accordance with this contract.

(7) Others are people or organisations who are not the *Employer*, the *Consultant*, the *Adjudicator* or any employee, Subconsultant or supplier of the *Consultant*.

(8) The Parties are the *Employer* and the *Consultant*.

(9) To Provide the Services means to do the work necessary to complete the *services* in accordance with this contract and all incidental work, services and actions which this contract requires.

core clauses

main option clauses

secondary option clauses

contract data

(10) The Risk Register is a register of the risks which are listed in the Contract Data and the risks which the *Employer* or the *Consultant* has notified as an early warning matter. It includes a description of the risk and a description of the actions which are to be taken to avoid or reduce the risk.

(11) The Scope is information which either

- specifies and describes the *services* or
- states any constraints on how the *Consultant* Provides the Services

and is either

- in the documents which the Contract Data states it is in or
- in an instruction given in accordance with this contract.

(12) A Subconsultant is a person or organisation who has a contract with the *Consultant* to provide part of the *services*.

(13) The Time Charge is the sum of the products of each of the *staff rates* multiplied by the total staff time appropriate to that rate properly spent on work in this contract.

Interpretation and the law **12**

12.1 In this contract, except where the context shows otherwise, words in the singular also mean in the plural and the other way round and words in the masculine also mean in the feminine and neuter.

12.2 This contract is governed by the *law of the contract*.

12.3 No change to this contract, unless provided for by the *conditions of contract*, has effect unless it has been agreed, confirmed in writing and signed by the Parties.

12.4 This contract is the entire agreement between the Parties.

Communications **13**

13.1 Each instruction, certificate, submission, proposal, record, acceptance, notification, reply and other communication which this contract requires is communicated in a form which can be read, copied and recorded. Writing is in the *language of this contract*.

13.2 A communication has effect when it is received at the last address notified by the recipient for receiving communications or, if none is notified, at the address of the recipient stated in the Contract Data.

13.3 If this contract requires the *Employer* or the *Consultant* to reply to a communication, unless otherwise stated in this contract, he replies within the *period for reply*.

13.4 The *Employer* replies to a communication submitted or resubmitted to him by the *Consultant* for acceptance. If his reply is not acceptance, the *Employer* states his reasons and the *Consultant* resubmits the communication within the *period for reply* taking account of these reasons. A reason for withholding acceptance is that more information is needed in order to assess the *Consultant*'s submission fully.

13.5 The *Employer* may extend the *period for reply* to a communication if the *Employer* and the *Consultant* agree to the extension before the reply is due. The *Employer* notifies the *Consultant* of the extension which has been agreed.

13.6 The *Consultant* retains copies of drawings, specifications, reports and other documents which record the *services* for the *period for retention*. The copies are retained in the form stated in the Scope.

13.7 A notification which this contract requires is communicated separately from other communications.

	13.8 The *Employer* may withhold acceptance of a submission by the *Consultant*. Withholding acceptance for a reason stated in this contract is not a compensation event.
Acceptance 14	
	14.1 The *Employer*'s acceptance of a communication from the *Consultant* or of his work does not change the *Consultant*'s responsibility to Provide the Services.
Early warning 15	

15.1 The *Employer* and the *Consultant* give an early warning by notifying the other as soon as either becomes aware of any matter which could

- increase the total of the Prices,
- delay Completion,
- change the Accepted Programme,
- delay meeting a Key Date,
- impair the usefulness of the *services* to the *Employer* or
- affect the work of the *Employer*, an *Employer*'s contractor or another consultant.

The *Consultant* may give an early warning by notifying the *Employer* of any other matter which could increase his total cost. The *Employer* enters early warning matters in the Risk Register. Early warning of a matter for which a compensation event has previously been notified is not required.

15.2 Either the *Employer* or the *Consultant* may instruct the other to attend a risk reduction meeting. Each may instruct other people to attend if the other Party agrees.

15.3 At a risk reduction meeting, those who attend co-operate in

- making and considering proposals for how the effect of the registered risks can be avoided or reduced,
- seeking solutions that will bring advantage to all those who will be affected,
- deciding on the actions which will be taken and who, in accordance with this contract, will take them and
- deciding which risks have now been avoided or have passed and can be removed from the Risk Register.

15.4 The *Employer* revises the Risk Register to record the decisions made at each risk reduction meeting and issues the revised Risk Register to the *Consultant*. If a decision needs a change to the Scope, the *Employer* instructs the change at the same time as he issues the revised Risk Register.

Ambiguities and 16
inconsistencies 16.1 The *Employer* or the *Consultant* notifies the other as soon as either becomes aware of an ambiguity or inconsistency in or between the documents which are part of this contract. The *Employer* gives an instruction resolving the ambiguity or inconsistency.

Illegal and impossible 17
requirements 17.1 The *Consultant* notifies the *Employer* as soon as he considers that the Scope requires him to do anything which is illegal or impossible. If the *Employer* agrees, he gives an instruction to change the Scope appropriately.

core clauses

main option clauses

secondary option clauses

contract data

Prevention 18

18.1   If an event occurs which

- stops the *Consultant* Providing the Service or
- stops the *Consultant* Providing the Service by the date shown on the Accepted Programme,

and which

- neither Party could prevent and
- an experienced consultant would have judged at the Contract Date to have such a small chance of occurring that it would have been unreasonable for him to have allowed for it,

the *Employer* gives an instruction to the *Consultant* stating how he is to deal with the event.

core
clauses

main
option clauses

secondary
option clauses

contract
data

2 The Parties' main responsibilities

The *Employer*'s obligations **20**

20.1 The *Employer* provides information and things which this contract requires him to provide in accordance with the Accepted Programme.

20.2 The *Employer* may give an instruction to the *Consultant* which changes the Scope or a Key Date. After Completion, an instruction is given only if it is necessary to Provide the Services.

20.3 The *Employer* does not give an instruction to the *Consultant* which would require him to act in a way that was outside his professional code of conduct.

The *Consultant*'s obligations **21**

21.1 The *Consultant* Provides the Services in accordance with the Scope.

21.2 The *Consultant*'s obligation is to use the skill and care normally used by professionals providing services similar to the *services*.

People **22**

22.1 The *Consultant* either employs each *key person* named to do the job for him stated in the Contract Data or employs a replacement person who has been accepted by the *Employer*. The *Consultant* submits the name, relevant qualifications and experience of a proposed replacement person to the *Employer* for acceptance. A reason for not accepting the person is that his relevant qualifications and experience are not as good as those of the person who is to be replaced.

22.2 The *Employer* may, having stated his reasons, instruct the *Consultant* to remove a person employed by the *Consultant*. The *Consultant* then arranges that, after one day, the person has no further connection with the work included in this contract.

Working with the *Employer* and Others **23**

23.1 The *Consultant* co-operates with Others in obtaining and providing information which they need in connection with the *services*.

23.2 Where necessary to Provide the Services, the *Consultant* holds or attends meetings with Others. The *Consultant* informs the *Employer* of these meetings beforehand and the *Employer* may attend them.

23.3 If the *Employer* decides that the work does not meet the Condition stated for a Key Date by the date stated and, as a result, the *Employer* incurs additional cost either

- in carrying out work or
- by paying an additional amount to Others in carrying out work

on the same project, the additional cost the *Employer* has paid or will incur is paid by the *Consultant*. The *Employer* assesses the additional cost within four weeks of the date when the Condition stated for that Key Date is met. The *Employer*'s right to recover the additional cost which is his only right in these circumstances.

Subconsulting **24**

24.1 If the *Consultant* subcontracts work, he is responsible for Providing the Services as if he had not subcontracted. This contract applies as if a Subconsultant's employees were the *Consultant*'s.

24.2 The *Consultant* submits the name of each proposed Subconsultant to the *Employer* for acceptance. A reason for not accepting the Subconsultant is that his appointment will not allow the *Consultant* to Provide the Services. The *Consultant* does not appoint a proposed Subconsultant until the *Employer* has accepted him.

24.3 The *Consultant* submits the proposed conditions of contract for each subcontract to the *Employer* for acceptance unless

- an NEC contract is proposed or
- the *Employer* has agreed that no submission is required.

The *Consultant* does not appoint a Subconsultant on the proposed subcontract conditions submitted until the *Employer* has accepted them. A reason for not accepting them is that

- they will not allow the *Consultant* to Provide the Services or
- they do not include a statement that the parties to the subcontract shall act in a spirit of mutual trust and co-operation.

Other responsibilities **25**

25.1 The *Consultant* obtains approval from Others where necessary to Provide the Services.

25.2 The *Employer* provides access to a person, place or thing to the *Consultant* as stated in the Contract Data on or before the later of its *access date* and the access date for it shown on the Accepted Programme.

25.3 The *Consultant* obeys an instruction which is in accordance with this contract and is given to him by the *Employer*.

25.4 The *Consultant* acts in accordance with the health and safety requirements stated in the Scope.

www.neccontract.com

3 Time

Starting, Completion and Key Dates **30**

30.1 The *Consultant* does not start work until the *starting date* and does the work so that Completion is on or before the Completion Date.

30.2 The *Employer* decides the date of Completion and certifies it within one week of the date.

30.3 The *Consultant* does the work so that the Condition stated for each Key Date is met by the Key Date.

The programme **31**

31.1 If a programme is not identified in the Contract Data, the *Consultant* submits a first programme to the *Employer* for acceptance within the period stated in the Contract Data.

31.2 The *Consultant* shows on each programme which he submits for acceptance

- the *starting date, access dates*, Key Dates and Completion Date,
- planned Completion,
- the order and timing of the operations which the *Consultant* plans to do in order to Provide the Services,
- the order and timing of the work of the *Employer* and Others as last agreed with them by the *Consultant* or, if not so agreed, as stated in the Scope,
- the dates when the *Consultant* plans to meet each Condition stated for the Key Dates and to complete other work needed to allow the *Employer* and Others to do their work,
- provisions for

  - float,
  - time risk allowances,
  - health and safety requirements and
  - the procedures set out in this contract,

- the dates when, in order to Provide the Services in accordance with his programme, the *Consultant* will need

  - access to a person, place or thing if later than its *access date*,
  - information and things to be provided by the *Employer* and
  - information and approval from Others,

- for each operation, a statement of how the *Consultant* plans to do the work identifying the resources which he plans to use and
- other information which the Scope requires the *Consultant* to show on a programme submitted for acceptance.

31.3 Within two weeks of the *Consultant* submitting a programme to him for acceptance, the *Employer* either accepts the programme or notifies the *Consultant* of his reasons for not accepting it. A reason for not accepting a programme is that

- the *Consultant*'s plans which it shows are not practicable,
- it does not show the information which this contract requires,
- it does not represent the *Consultant*'s plans realistically or
- it does not comply with the Scope.

core clauses

main option clauses

secondary option clauses

contract data

Revising the programme **32**

32.1 The *Consultant* shows on each revised programme

- the actual progress achieved on each operation and its effect upon the timing of the remaining work,
- the effects of implemented compensation events,
- how the *Consultant* plans to deal with any delays and to correct notified Defects and
- any other changes which the *Consultant* proposes to make to the Accepted Programme.

32.2 The *Consultant* submits a revised programme to the *Employer* for acceptance

- within the *period for reply* after the *Employer* has instructed him to,
- when the *Consultant* chooses to and, in any case,
- at no longer interval than the interval stated in the Contract Data from the *starting date* until Completion of the whole of the *services*.

Instructions to stop or not to start work **33**

33.1 The *Employer* may instruct the *Consultant* to stop or not to start any work and may later instruct him that he may re-start or start it.

Acceleration **34**

34.1 The *Employer* may instruct the *Consultant* to submit a quotation for acceleration to achieve Completion before the Completion Date. The *Employer* states changes to the Key Dates to be included in the quotation. A quotation for an acceleration comprises proposed changes to the Prices and a revised programme showing the earlier Completion Date and the changed Key Dates. The *Consultant* submits details of his assessment with each quotation.

34.2 The *Consultant* submits a quotation or gives his reasons for not doing so within the *period for reply*.

core clauses / main option clauses / secondary option clauses / contract data

4 Quality

Quality management system **40**

40.1 The *Consultant* operates a quality management system for Providing the Services as stated in the Scope. The quality management system complies with the requirements stated in the Scope.

40.2 The *Consultant* provides the *Employer,* within the period stated in the Contract Data, with a quality policy statement and a quality plan for acceptance. The quality policy statement and quality plan comply with the requirements stated in the Scope.

40.3 The *Consultant* complies with an instruction from the *Employer* to the *Consultant* to correct a failure to comply with the quality plan.

Correcting Defects **41**

41.1 Until the *defects date*, the *Employer* notifies the *Consultant* of each Defect as soon as he finds it and the *Consultant* notifies the *Employer* of each Defect as soon as he finds it. At Completion the *Consultant* notifies the *Employer* of the Defects which have not been corrected. After Completion and until the *defects date*, the *Consultant* notifies the *Employer* of each Defect as soon as he finds it. The *Employer*'s rights in respect of a Defect which the *Employer* has not found or notified by the *defects date* are not affected.

41.2 The *Consultant* corrects a Defect whether or not the *Employer* notifies him of it. The *Consultant* corrects Defects within a time which minimises the adverse effect on the *Employer* or Others. If the *Consultant* does not correct a Defect within the time required by this contract, the *Employer* assesses the cost to him of having the Defect corrected by other people and the *Consultant* pays this amount.

core clauses

main option clauses

secondary option clauses

contract data

5 Payment

Assessing the amount due **50**

50.1 The *Consultant* assesses the amount due and submits an invoice at each assessment date. The first assessment date is decided by the *Consultant* to suit the procedures of the Parties and is not later than the *assessment interval* after the *starting date*. Later assessment dates occur

- at the end of each *assessment interval* until eight weeks after the *defects date* and
- at Completion of the whole of the *services*.

50.2 Invoices submitted by the *Consultant* include the details stated in the Scope to show how the amount due has been assessed. The first invoice is for the amount due. Other invoices are for the change in the amount due since the previous invoice.

50.3 The amount due is

- the Price for Services Provided to Date,
- the amount of the *expenses* properly spent by the *Consultant* in Providing the Services and
- other amounts to be paid to the *Consultant* less amounts to be paid by or retained from the *Consultant*.

Any tax which the law requires the *Employer* to pay to the *Consultant* is included in the amount due.

Payment **51**

51.1 Each payment is made within three weeks of receiving the *Consultant*'s invoice or, if a different period is stated in the Contract Data, within the period stated. Each payment is the amount due less previous payments.

51.2 Payments are in the *currency of this contract* unless otherwise stated in this contract.

51.3 If the *Employer* does not accept the *Consultant*'s assessment of the amount due, he notifies the *Consultant* of his reasons and the amount which he assesses is due before the payment becomes due. He pays the amount of his assessment. The agreed part of the invoice is paid. The *Consultant* either

- corrects the invoice to a sum agreed by the *Employer* or
- provides further information to justify the invoice.

51.4 If a payment is late or has been delayed because of a disagreement, interest is paid. Interest is assessed from the date by which the late payment should have been made until the date when the late payment is made, and is included in the first assessment after the late payment is made.

51.5 Interest is calculated on a daily basis at the *interest rate* and is compounded annually.

core clauses

main option clauses

secondary option clauses

contract data

6 Compensation events

Compensation events **60**

60.1 The following are compensation events.

(1) The *Employer* gives an instruction changing the Scope.

(2) The *Employer* does not provide access to a person, place or thing for the *Consultant* as stated in this contract.

(3) The *Employer* does not provide something which he is to provide by the date for providing it shown on the Accepted Programme.

(4) The *Employer* gives an instruction to stop or not to start any work or to change a Key Date.

(5) The *Employer* or Others do not work within the times shown on the Accepted Programme or within the conditions stated in the Scope.

(6) The *Employer* does not reply to a communication from the *Consultant* within the period required by this contract.

(7) The *Employer* changes a decision which he has previously communicated to the *Consultant*.

(8) The *Employer* withholds an acceptance (other than acceptance of a quotation for acceleration) for a reason not stated in this contract.

(9) The *Employer* notifies a correction to an assumption which he has stated about a compensation event.

(10) A breach of contract by the *Employer* which is not one of the other compensation events in this contract.

(11) An event which

- stops the *Consultant* completing the *services* or
- stops the *Consultant* completing the *services* by the date shown on the Accepted Programme,

and which

- neither Party could prevent,
- an experienced consultant would have judged at the Contract Date to have such a small chance of occurring that it would have been unreasonable for him to have allowed for it and
- is not one of the other compensation events stated in this contract.

(12) The *Consultant* corrects a Defect for which he is not liable under this contract.

Notifying compensation **61**
events 61.1 For compensation events which arise from the *Employer* giving an instruction or changing an earlier decision, the *Employer* notifies the *Consultant* of the compensation event at the time of giving the instruction or changing the earlier decision. He also instructs the *Consultant* to submit quotations, unless the event arises from a fault of the *Consultant* or quotations have already been submitted. The *Consultant* puts the instruction or changed decision into effect.

61.2 The *Employer* may instruct the *Consultant* to submit quotations for a proposed instruction or a proposed changed decision. The *Consultant* does not put a proposed instruction or a proposed changed decision into effect.

61.3 The *Consultant* notifies the *Employer* of an event which has happened or which he expects to happen as a compensation event if

- the *Consultant* believes that the event is a compensation event and
- the *Employer* has not notified the event to the *Consultant*.

If the *Consultant* does not notify a compensation event within eight weeks of becoming aware of the event, he is not entitled to a change in Prices, the Completion Date or a Key Date unless the *Employer* should have notified the event to the *Consultant* but did not.

61.4 If the *Employer* decides that an event notified by the *Consultant*

- arises from a fault of the *Consultant*,
- has not happened and is not expected to happen,
- has no effect upon the *Consultant*'s costs, Completion or meeting a Key Date or
- is not one of the compensation events stated in this contract

he notifies the *Consultant* of his decision that the Prices, the Completion Date and the Key Date are not to be changed.

If the *Employer* decides otherwise, he notifies the *Consultant* accordingly and instructs him to submit quotations.

If the *Employer* does not notify his decision to the *Consultant* within either

- one week of the *Consultant*'s notification or
- a longer period to which the *Consultant* has agreed,

the *Consultant* may notify the *Employer* to this effect. A failure by the *Employer* to reply within two weeks of this notification is treated as acceptance by the *Employer* that the event is a compensation event and an instruction to submit quotations.

61.5 If the *Employer* decides that the *Consultant* did not give an early warning of the event which an experienced consultant could have given, he notifies this decision to the *Consultant* when he instructs him to submit quotations.

61.6 If the *Employer* decides that the effects of a compensation event are too uncertain to be forecast reasonably, he states assumptions about the event in his instruction to the *Consultant* to submit quotations. Assessment of the event is based on these assumptions. If any of them is later found to have been wrong, the *Employer* notifies a correction.

61.7 A compensation event is not notified after the *defects date*.

Quotations for **62**
compensation events 62.1 After discussing with the *Consultant* different ways of dealing with the compensation event which are practicable, the *Employer* may instruct the *Consultant* to submit alternative quotations. The *Consultant* submits the required quotations to the *Employer* and may submit quotations for other methods of dealing with the compensation event which he considers practicable.

62.2 Quotations for compensation events comprise proposed changes to the Prices and any delay to the Completion Date and Key Dates assessed by the *Consultant*. The *Consultant* submits details of his assessment with each quotation. If the programme for remaining work is altered by the compensation event, the *Consultant* includes the alterations to the Accepted Programme in his quotation.

core clauses

main option clauses

secondary option clauses

contract data

62.3   The *Consultant* submits quotations within two weeks of being instructed to do so by the *Employer*. The *Employer* replies within two weeks of the submission. His reply is

- an instruction to submit a revised quotation,
- an acceptance of a quotation,
- a notification that a proposed instruction will not be given or a proposed changed decision will not be made or
- a notification that he will be making his own assessment.

62.4   The *Employer* instructs the *Consultant* to submit a revised quotation only after explaining his reasons for doing so to the *Consultant*. The *Consultant* submits the revised quotation within three weeks of being instructed to do so.

62.5   The *Employer* extends the time allowed for

- the *Consultant* to submit quotations for a compensation event and
- the *Employer* to reply to a quotation

if the *Employer* and the *Consultant* agree to the extension before the submission or reply is due. The *Employer* notifies the extension that has been agreed to the *Consultant*.

62.6   If the *Employer* does not reply to a quotation within the time allowed, the *Consultant* may notify the *Employer* to this effect. If the *Consultant* submitted more than one quotation for the compensation event, he states in his notification which quotation he proposes is to be accepted. If the *Employer* does not reply to the notification within two weeks and, unless the quotation is for a proposed instruction or a proposed changed decision, the *Consultant*'s notification is treated as acceptance of the quotation by the *Employer*.

Assessing compensation events   **63**

63.1   The changes to the Prices are assessed as the effect of the compensation event upon

- the actual Time Charge for the work already done and
- the forecast Time Charge for the work not yet done.

The date when the *Employer* instructed or should have instructed the *Consultant* to submit quotations divides the work already done from the work not yet done.

63.2   If the effect of a compensation event is to reduce the total Time Charge, the Prices are not reduced excepted as stated in this contract.

63.3   A delay to the Completion Date is assessed as the length of time that, due to the compensation event, planned Completion is later than planned Completion as shown on the Accepted Programme. A delay to a Key Date is assessed as the length of time that, due to the compensation event, the planned date when the Condition stated for a Key Date will be met is later than the date shown on the Accepted Programme.

63.4   The rights of the *Employer* and the *Consultant* to changes to the Prices, the Completion Date and the Key Dates are their only rights in respect of a compensation event.

63.5   If the *Employer* has notified the *Consultant* of his decision that the *Consultant* did not give an early warning of a compensation event which an experienced consultant could have given, the event is assessed as if the *Consultant* had given early warning.

63.6   Assessment of the effect of a compensation event includes risk allowances for cost and time for matters which have a significant chance of occurring and are at the *Consultant*'s risk under this contract.

63.7   Assessments for work not yet done are based upon the assumptions that the *Consultant* will react competently and promptly to the compensation event and that the Accepted Programme can be changed. Assessments for work already done include only cost and time which were reasonably incurred.

core clauses

main option clauses

secondary option clauses

contract data

63.8 A compensation event which is an instruction to change the Scope in order to resolve an ambiguity or inconsistency is assessed as if the Prices, the Completion Date and the Key Dates were for the interpretation most favourable to the Party which did not provide the Scope.

63.9 If a change to the Scope makes the description of the Condition for a Key Date incorrect, the *Employer* corrects the description. This correction is taken into account in assessing the compensation event for the change to the Scope.

63.10 If the work included in a quotation for a compensation event includes work by staff for which there is no *staff rate*, a proposed rate is included in the quotation.

63.11 The following are deducted from the assessment of compensation events

- the cost of events for which this contract requires the *Consultant* to insure and
- other costs paid to the *Consultant* by insurers.

The *Employer*'s 64
assessments 64.1 The *Employer* assesses a compensation event

- if the *Consultant* has not submitted a required quotation and details of his assessment within the time allowed,
- if the *Employer* decides that the *Consultant* has not assessed the compensation event correctly in a quotation and he does not instruct the *Consultant* to submit a revised quotation,
- if, when the *Consultant* submits quotations for a compensation event, he has not submitted a programme or alterations to a programme which this contract requires him to submit or
- if, when the *Consultant* submits quotations for a compensation event, the *Employer* has not accepted the *Consultant*'s latest programme for one of the reasons stated in this contract.

64.2 The *Employer* assesses a compensation event using his own assessment of the programme for the remaining work if

- there is no Accepted Programme or
- the *Consultant* has not submitted a programme or alterations to a programme for acceptance as required by this contract.

64.3 The *Employer* notifies the *Consultant* of his assessment of a compensation event and gives him details of it within the period allowed for the *Consultant*'s submission of his quotation for the same event. This period starts when the need for the *Employer*'s assessment becomes apparent.

64.4 If the *Employer* does not assess a compensation event within the time allowed, the *Consultant* may notify the *Employer* to this effect. If the *Consultant* submitted more than one quotation for the compensation event, he states in his notification which quotation he proposes is to be accepted. If the *Employer* does not reply within two weeks of this notification the notification is treated as acceptance of the *Consultant*'s quotation by the *Employer*.

Implementing 65
compensation events 65.1 A compensation event is implemented when

- the *Employer* notifies his acceptance of the *Consultant*'s quotation,
- the *Employer* notifies the *Consultant* of his own assessment or
- a *Consultant*'s quotation is treated as having been accepted by the *Employer*.

65.2 The assessment of a compensation event is not revised if a forecast upon which it is based is shown by later recorded information to have been wrong.

7 Rights to material

The Parties' use of material **70**

70.1 The *Employer* has the right to use the material provided by the *Consultant* for the purpose stated in the Scope. The *Consultant* obtains from a Subconsultant equivalent rights for the *Employer* to use material prepared by the Subconsultant.

70.2 The *Consultant* has the right to use material provided by the *Employer* only to Provide the Services. The *Consultant* may make this right available to a Subconsultant. On Completion of the whole of the *services*, the *Consultant* returns the material provided by the *Employer* to him.

70.3 The Parties do not disclose information obtained in connection with the *services* except when necessary to carry out their duties under this contract.

70.4 The *Consultant* may use the material provided by him under this contract for other work unless stated otherwise in the Scope.

Publicity **71**

71.1 The *Consultant* may publicise the *services* only with the *Employer*'s written agreement.

core clauses

main option clauses

secondary option clauses

contract data

8 Indemnity, insurance and liability

Indemnity 80

80.1 The *Consultant* indemnifies the *Employer* against claims, proceedings, compensation and costs payable arising out of an infringement by the *Consultant* of the rights of Others, except an infringement which arose out of the use by the *Consultant* of things provided by the *Employer*.

Insurance cover 81

81.1 The *Consultant* provides the insurances stated in the Insurance Table except any insurance which the *Employer* is to provide as stated in the Contract Data. The insurances provide cover from the Contract Date until the end of the periods stated in the Contract Data.

INSURANCE TABLE

Insurance against	Minimum amount of cover
Liability of the *Consultant* for claims made against him arising out of his failure to use the skill and care normally used by professionals providing services similar to the *services*	The amount stated in the Contract Data
Liability for death of or bodily injury to a person (not an employee of the *Consultant*) or loss of or damage to property resulting from an action or failure to take action by the *Consultant*	The amount stated in the Contract Data for any one event
Liability for death of or bodily injury to employees of the *Consultant* arising out of and in the course of their employment in connection with this contract	The greater of the amount required by the applicable law and the amount stated in the Contract Data for any one event

81.2 When requested by a Party the other Party provides certificates from his insurer or broker stating that the insurances required by this contract are in force.

Limitation of liability 82

82.1 The *Consultant*'s total liability to the *Employer* for all matters arising under or in connection with this contract, other than the excluded matters, is limited to the amount stated in the Contract Data and applies in contract, tort or delict and otherwise to the extent allowed under the *law of the contract*.

The excluded matters are amounts payable by the *Consultant* as stated in this contract for

- delay damages if Option X7 applies,
- *Consultant*'s share if Option C applies,
- an infringement by the *Consultant* of the rights of Others,
- loss of or damage to third party property and
- death of or bodily injury to a person other than an employee of the *Consultant*.

82.2 The *Consultant*'s liability to the *Employer* is limited to that proportion of the *Employer*'s losses for which the *Consultant* is responsible under this contract.

                                    www.neccontract.com

9 Termination

Termination **90**

90.1 Either Party may terminate the *Consultant's* obligation to Provide the Services by notifying the other Party if the other Party has done one of the following or its equivalent.

- If the other Party is an individual and has

  - presented his petition for bankruptcy,
  - had a bankruptcy order made against him,
  - had a receiver appointed over his assets or
  - made an arrangement with his creditors.

- If the other Party is a company or partnership and has

  - had a winding-up order made against it,
  - had a provisional liquidator appointed to it,
  - passed a resolution for winding-up (other than in order to amalgamate or reconstruct),
  - had an administration order made against it,
  - had a receiver, receiver and manager, or administrative receiver appointed over the whole or a substantial part of its undertaking or assets or
  - made an arrangement with its creditors.

90.2 The *Consultant* may terminate his obligation to Provide the Services by notifying the *Employer* if the *Employer* has not paid an amount due to the *Consultant* within eight weeks of the issue of a notice by the *Consultant* to the *Employer* that payment is overdue.

90.3 The *Employer* may terminate the *Consultant's* obligation to Provide the Services by notifying the *Consultant* if

- the *Employer* no longer requires the *services* or
- the *Consultant* has substantially failed to comply with his obligations and has not put the default right within four weeks of a notification by the *Employer*.

90.4 The *Employer* may terminate the *Consultant's* obligation to Provide the Services by notifying the *Consultant* if an event occurs which

- stops the *Consultant* completing the *services* or
- stops the *Consultant* completing the *services* by the date shown on the Accepted Programme and is forecast to delay Completion by more than 13 weeks,

and which

- neither Party could prevent and
- an experienced consultant would have judged at the Contract Date to have such a small chance of occurring that it would have been unreasonable for him to have allowed for it.

Procedures on termination **91**

91.1 On termination

- the *Consultant* does no further work necessary to Provide the Services,
- the *Employer* may complete the *services* and may use any material to which he has title,
- the *Employer* may require the *Consultant* to assign the benefit of any subconsultancy or other contract related to performance of this contract to the *Employer* and
- the Parties continue to comply with the constraints and obligations in this contract on

  - the use of material prepared or obtained by the *Consultant* and
  - publicising the *services*.

After the final payment has been made, the *Consultant* gives to the *Employer* information resulting from work carried out to date and information the *Consultant* has obtained which he has a responsibility to provide under this contract.

Payment on termination **92**

92.1 A final payment is made as soon as possible after termination. The amount due on termination includes

- an amount due assessed as for normal payments and
- other costs reasonably incurred by the *Consultant* in expectation of completing the whole of the *services* and to which the *Consultant* is committed.

92.2 If the *Employer* terminates because of the

- insolvency of the *Consultant* or
- substantial failure of the *Consultant* to comply with his obligations,

the amount due on termination includes a deduction of the forecast of the additional cost to the *Employer* of completing the whole of the *services*.

MAIN OPTION CLAUSES

Option A: Priced contract with activity schedule

Identified and defined terms **11**

11.2 (14) The Activity Schedule is the *activity schedule* unless later changed in accordance with this contract.

(15) The Price for Services Provided to Date is the total of the Prices for the activities which have been completed. A completed activity is one which is without Defects which would delay immediately following work.

(18) The Prices are the lump sum prices for each of the activities on the Activity Schedule unless later changed in accordance with this contract.

The *Consultant*'s obligations **21**

21.3 The *Consultant* prepares forecasts of the total *expenses* for the whole of the *services* and submits them to the *Employer*. Forecasts are prepared at the intervals stated in the Contract Data from the *starting date* until Completion of the whole of the *services*. An explanation of the changes made since the previous forecast is submitted with each forecast.

The programme **31**

31.4 The *Consultant* provides information which shows how each activity on the Activity Schedule relates to the operations on each programme which he submits for acceptance.

Acceleration **34**

34.3 When the *Employer* accepts a quotation for an acceleration, he changes the Prices, the Completion Date and the Key Dates accordingly and accepts the revised programme.

Accounts and records **52**

52.1 The *Consultant* keeps accounts and records of his *expenses* and allows the *Employer* to inspect them at any time within working hours.

The Activity Schedule **53**

53.1 Information in the Activity Schedule is not Scope.

53.2 If the *Consultant* changes a planned method of completing the *services* at his discretion so that the Activity Schedule does not comply with the Accepted Programme, he submits a revision of the Activity Schedule to the *Employer* for acceptance.

53.3 A reason for not accepting a revision of the Activity Schedule is that

- it does not comply with the Accepted Programme,
- any changed Prices are not reasonably distributed between the activities or
- the total of the Prices is changed.

Quotations for compensation events **62**

62.7 The cost of preparing quotations for compensation events is not included in the assessment of compensation events.

Assessing compensation	63	
events	63.12	If the effect of a compensation event is to reduce the total Time Charge and the event is

- a change to the Scope or
- a correction of an assumption stated by the *Employer* for assessing an earlier compensation event,

the Prices are reduced.

63.14 Assessments for changed Prices for compensation events are in the form of changes to the Activity Schedule.

Implementing	65	
compensation events	65.3	The changes to the Prices, the Completion Date and the Key Dates are included in the notification implementing a compensation event.

Option C: Target contract

Identified and defined terms	**11**	
	11.2	(14) The Activity Schedule is the *activity schedule* unless later changed in accordance with this contract.
		(16) The Price for Services Provided to Date is the Time Charge for the work which has been completed.
		(18) The Prices are the lump sum prices for each of the activities on the Activity Schedule unless later changed in accordance with this contract.
The *Consultant*'s obligations	**21**	
	21.4	The *Consultant* prepares forecasts of the total Time Charge and *expenses* for the whole of the *services* and submits them to the *Employer*. Forecasts are prepared at the intervals stated in the Contract Data from the *starting date* until Completion of the whole of the *services*. An explanation of the changes made since the previous forecast is submitted with each forecast.
Subconsulting	**24**	
	24.4	The *Consultant* submits the proposed contract data for each subcontract for acceptance to the *Employer* if

- an NEC contract is proposed and
- the *Employer* instructs the *Consultant* to make the submission.

A reason for not accepting the proposed contract data is that its use will not allow the *Consultant* to Provide the Services.

The programme	**31**	
	31.4	The *Consultant* provides information which shows how each activity on the Activity Schedule relates to the operations on each programme which he submits for acceptance.
Acceleration	**34**	
	34.3	When the *Employer* accepts a quotation for an acceleration, he changes the Prices, the Completion Date and the Key Dates accordingly and accepts the revised programme.
Assessing the amount due	**50**	
	50.4	Payments for staff whose *staff rate* is stated in the Contract Data in a currency other than the *currency of this contract* are included in the amount due as payments to be made to the *Consultant* in the same currency. Such payments are converted to the *currency of this contract* in order to calculate the *Consultant*'s share using the *exchange rates*.
Accounts and records	**52**	
	52.2	The *Consultant* keeps accounts and records of his Time Charge and *expenses* and allows the *Employer* to inspect them at any time within working hours.

core clauses

main option clauses

secondary option clauses

contract data

The Activity Schedule	**53**	
	53.1	Information in the Activity Schedule is not Scope.
	53.2	If the *Consultant* changes a planned method of completing the *services* at his discretion so that the Activity Schedule does not comply with the Accepted Programme, he submits a revision of the Activity Schedule to the *Employer* for acceptance.
	53.3	A reason for not accepting a revision of the Activity Schedule is that

- it does not comply with the Accepted Programme,
- any changed Prices are not reasonably distributed between the activities or
- the total of the Prices is changed.

The *Consultant*'s share	**54**	
	54.1	The *Employer* assesses the *Consultant*'s share of the difference between the total of the Prices and the Price for Services Provided to Date. The difference is divided into increments falling within each of the *share ranges*. The limits of a *share range* are the Price for Services Provided to Date divided by the total of the Prices, expressed as a percentage. The *Consultant*'s share equals the sum of the products of the increment within each *share range* and the corresponding *Consultant's share percentage*.
	54.2	If the Price for Services Provided to Date is less than the total of the Prices, the *Consultant* is paid his share of the saving. If the Price for Services Provided to Date is greater than the total of the Prices, the *Consultant* pays his share of the excess.
	54.3	The *Employer* makes a preliminary assessment of the *Consultant*'s share at Completion of the whole of the *services* using his forecasts of the final Price for Services Provided to Date and the final total of the Prices. This share is included in the amount due following Completion of the whole of the *services*.
	54.4	The *Employer* makes a final assessment of the *Consultant*'s share using the final Price for Services Provided to Date and the final total of the Prices. This share is included in the final amount due.

Assessing compensation events	**63**	
	63.13	If the effect of a compensation event is to reduce the total Time Charge and the event is

- a change to the Scope, other than a change to the Scope which the *Consultant* proposed and the *Employer* has accepted or
- a correction of an assumption stated by the *Employer* for assessing an earlier compensation event,

the Prices are reduced.

	63.14	Assessments for changed Prices for compensation events are in the form of changes to the Activity Schedule.

Implementing compensation events	**65**	
	65.3	The changes to the Prices, the Completion Date and the Key Dates are included in the notification implementing a compensation event.

Payment on termination	**92**	
	92.3	If there is a termination, the *Employer* assesses the *Consultant*'s share. His assessment uses as the Price for Services Provided to Date the total of the Time Charge which the *Consultant* has paid and which he is committed to pay for work done before termination.

The *Employer*'s assessment of the *Consultant*'s share is added to the amount due to the *Consultant* on termination if there has been a saving or deducted if there has been an excess.

Option E: Time based contract

Identified and defined terms	**11** 11.2

Identified and defined terms 11

11.2 (16) The Price for Services Provided to Date is the Time Charge for the work which has been completed.

(19) The Prices are the Time Charge.

The *Consultant*'s obligations 21

21.4 The *Consultant* prepares forecasts of the total Time Charge and *expenses* for the whole of the *services* and submits them to the *Employer*. Forecasts are prepared at the intervals stated in the Contract Data from the *starting date* until Completion of the whole of the *services*. An explanation of the changes made since the previous forecast is submitted with each forecast.

Subconsulting 24

24.4 The *Consultant* submits the proposed contract data for each subcontract for acceptance to the *Employer* if

- an NEC contract is proposed and
- the *Employer* instructs the *Consultant* to make the submission.

A reason for not accepting the proposed contract data is that its use will not allow the *Consultant* to Provide the Services.

Acceleration 34

34.4 When the *Employer* accepts a quotation for an acceleration, he changes the Completion Date, the Key Dates and the forecast of the total Time Charge for the whole of the *services* accordingly and accepts the revised programme.

Assessing the amount due 50

50.5 Payments for staff whose *staff rate* is stated in the Contract Data in a currency other than the *currency of this contract* are included in the amount due as payments to be made to the *Consultant* in the same currency.

Accounts and records 52

52.2 The *Consultant* keeps accounts and records of his Time Charge and *expenses* and allows the *Employer* to inspect them at any time within working hours.

Implementing compensation events 65

65.4 The changes to the forecast amount of the Prices, the Completion Date and the Key Dates are included in the notification implementing a compensation event.

core clauses

main option clauses

secondary option clauses

contract data

Option G: Term contract

Identified and defined terms **11**

11.2 (17) The Price for Services Provided to Date is, for each Task, the total of

- the Time Charge for work which has been completed on time based items on the Task Schedule and
- a proportion of the lump sum price for each other item on the Task Schedule which is the proportion of work completed on that item.

(20) The Prices are

- the Time Charge for items described as time based on the Task Schedule and
- the lump sum price in the Task Schedule for each other item.

(21) A Task is work within the *services* which the *Employer* may instruct the *Consultant* to carry out within a stated period of time.

(22) Task Completion is when the *Consultant* has done all the work which the Task Order requires him to do by the Task Completion Date, and corrected Defects which would have prevented the *Employer* or Others from using the *services* and Others from doing their work.

(23) Task Completion Date is the date for completion stated in the Task Order unless later changed in accordance with this contract.

(24) A Task Order is the *Employer*'s instruction to carry out a Task.

(25) The Task Schedule is the *task schedule* unless later changed in accordance with this contract.

The *Consultant*'s obligations **21**

21.4 The *Consultant* prepares forecasts of the total Time Charge and *expenses* for the whole of the *services* and submits them to the *Employer*. Forecasts are prepared at the intervals stated in the Contract Data from the *starting date* until Completion of the whole of the *services*. An explanation of the changes made since the previous forecast is submitted with each forecast.

The programme **31**

31.5 The *Consultant* provides information which shows how each item included in a Task relates to the operations on each programme which he submits for acceptance.

Assessing the amount due **50**

50.6 Payments for

- staff whose *staff rate* in the Contract Data or
- items whose prices in the Task Schedule are stated

in a currency other than *currency of this contract* are included in the amount due as payments to be made to the *Consultant* in the same currency.

Accounts and records **52**

52.2 The *Consultant* keeps accounts and records of his Time Charge and *expenses* and allows the *Employer* to inspect them at any time within working hours.

Assessing Tasks **55**

55.1   A Task Order includes

- a detailed description of the work in the Task,
- a priced list of items of work in the Task in which items taken from the Task Schedule are identified,
- the starting and completion dates for the Task,
- the amount of delay damages for late completion of the Task and
- the total of the Prices for the Task.

The *Employer* consults the *Consultant* about the contents of a Task Order before he issues it.

55.2   The delay damages in a Task Order, if any, are not more than the estimated cost to the *Employer* of late completion of the Task.

The Prices for items in the Task price list which are not taken from the Task Schedule are assessed in the same way as compensation events.

55.3   The *Consultant* does not start any work included in the Task until he has received the Task Order, and does the work so that Task Completion is on or before the Task Completion Date. No Task Order is issued after the Completion Date.

Compensation events **60**

60.1   The following are compensation events.

(13) The *Employer* issues an instruction changing a Task Order. If the effect of a compensation event which is an instruction changing a Task Order is to reduce the total Time Charge, the Prices are reduced.

(14) The *Consultant* receives the Task Order after the starting date stated in the Task Order.

(15) A Task Completion Date is later than the Completion Date.

60.2   The *Employer* corrects mistakes in the Task Schedule which arise from an ambiguity or inconsistency in or between the documents which are part of this contract. Each such correction is a compensation event.

Quotations for **62**
compensation events 62.7   The cost of preparing quotations for compensation events is not included in the assessment of compensation events.

Assessing compensation **63**
events 63.16   A delay to the Task Completion Date is assessed as the length of time that due to the compensation event, planned Task Completion is delayed.

63.17   Assessments for changed Prices for compensation events are in the form of changes to the Task Schedule.

63.18   If the effect of a compensation event is to reduce the total Time Charge and the event is

- a change to the Task or
- a correction of an assumption stated by the *Employer* for assessing an earlier compensation event,

the Prices are reduced.

Implementing **65**
compensation events 65.5   The *Employer* includes the changes to

- the Prices and the Task Completion Date and
- the final total of the Prices for the Task and the programme for the Task

from the quotation which he has accepted or from his own assessment in the notification implementing a compensation event.

core clauses

main option clauses

secondary option clauses

contract data

DISPUTE RESOLUTION

Option W1

Dispute resolution procedure (used unless the United Kingdom Housing Grants, Construction and Regeneration Act 1996 applies).

Dispute resolution **W1**

W1.1 A dispute arising under or in connection with this contract is referred to and decided by the *Adjudicator*.

The *Adjudicator* W1.2 (1) The Parties appoint the *Adjudicator* under the NEC Adjudicator's Contract current at the *starting date*.

(2) The *Adjudicator* acts impartially and decides the dispute as an independent adjudicator and not as an arbitrator.

(3) If the *Adjudicator* is not identified in the Contract Data or if the *Adjudicator* resigns or is unable to act, the Parties may choose an adjudicator jointly. If the Parties have not chosen an adjudicator, either Party may ask the *Adjudicators nominating body* to choose one. The *Adjudicator nominating body* chooses an adjudicator within four days of the request The chosen adjudicator becomes the *Adjudicator*.

(4) A replacement *Adjudicator* has the power to decide a dispute referred to his predecessor but not decided at the time when the predecessor resigned or became unable to act. He deals with an undecided dispute as if it had been referred to him on the date he was appointed.

(5) The *Adjudicator*, his employees and agents are not liable to the Parties for any action or failure to take action in an adjudication unless the action or failure to take action was in bad faith.

The adjudication W1.3 (1) Disputes are notified and referred to the *Adjudicator* in accordance with the Adjudication Table.

ADJUDICATION TABLE

Dispute about	Which Party may refer it to the *Adjudicator*?	When may it be referred to the *Adjudicator*?
An action of the *Employer*	The *Consultant*	Between two and four weeks after the *Consultant*'s notification of the dispute to the *Employer*, the notification itself being made not more than four weeks after the *Consultant* becomes aware of the action
The *Employer* not having taken an action	The *Consultant*	Between two and four weeks after the *Consultant*'s notification of the dispute to the *Employer*, the notification itself being made not more than four weeks after the *Consultant* becomes aware that the action was not taken
A quotation for a compensation event which is treated as having been accepted	The *Employer*	Between two and four weeks after the *Employer*'s notification of the dispute to the *Consultant*, the notification itself being made not more than four weeks after the quotation was treated as accepted
Any other matter	Either Party	Between two and four weeks after notification of the dispute to the other Party

(2) The times for notifying and referring a dispute may be extended if the *Consultant* and the *Employer* agree to the extension before the notice or referral is due. If a disputed matter is not notified and referred within the times set out in this contract, neither Party may subsequently refer it to the *Adjudicator* or the *tribunal*.

(3) The Party referring the dispute to the *Adjudicator* includes with his referral information to be considered by the *Adjudicator*. Any more information from a Party to be considered by the *Adjudicator* is provided within four weeks of the referral. This period may be extended if the *Adjudicator* and the Parties agree.

(4a) If a matter disputed by the *Consultant* under or in connection with a subcontract is also a matter disputed under or in connection with this contract and if the subcontract allows, the *Consultant* may refer the subcontract dispute to the *Adjudicator* at the same time as the main contract referral. The *Adjudicator* then decides the disputes together and references to the Parties for the purposes of the dispute are interpreted as including the Subconsultant.

(4b) If this contract is a subcontract and the main contract provides for joint adjudication of disputes, the following procedure applies.

Within two weeks of the notification of the dispute by the *Consultant* to the *Employer*, the *Employer* notifies the *Consultant* if the matter disputed is a matter disputed under or in connection with the main contract.

The *Employer* may then

- submit the subcontract dispute to the main contract Adjudicator at the same time as the main contract submission and
- instruct the *Consultant* to provide any information which the *Employer* may require.

The main contract *Adjudicator* then gives his decision on the disputes together.

(5) The *Adjudicator* may

- review and revise any action or inaction of the *Employer* related to the dispute and alter a quotation which has been treated as having been accepted,
- take the initiative in ascertaining the facts and the law related to the dispute,
- instruct a Party to provide further information related to the dispute within a stated time and
- instruct a Party to take any other action which he considers necessary to reach his decision and to do so within a stated time.

(6) A communication between a Party and the *Adjudicator* is communicated to the other Party at the same time.

(7) If the *Adjudicator's* decision includes assessment of additional cost or delay caused to the *Consultant*, he makes his assessment in the same way as a compensation event is assessed.

(8) The *Adjudicator* decides the dispute and notifies the Parties of his decision and his reasons within four weeks of the end of the period for receiving information. This four week period may be extended if the Parties agree.

(9) Unless and until the *Adjudicator* has notified the Parties of his decision, the Parties proceed as if the matter disputed was not disputed.

(10) The *Adjudicator's* decision is binding on the Parties unless and until revised by the *tribunal* and is enforceable as a matter of contractual obligation between the Parties and not as an arbitral award. The *Adjudicator's* decision is final and binding if neither Party has notified the other within the times required by this contract that he is dissatisfied with a decision of the *Adjudicator* and intends to refer the matter to the *tribunal*.

(11) The *Adjudicator* may, within two weeks of giving his decision to the Parties, correct any clerical mistake or ambiguity.

Review by the *tribunal* W1.4

(1) A Party does not refer any dispute under or in connection with this contract to the *tribunal* unless it has first been referred to the *Adjudicator* in accordance with this contract.

(2) If, after the *Adjudicator* notifies his decision a Party is dissatisfied, he may notify the other Party that he intends to refer it to the *tribunal*. A Party may not refer a dispute to the *tribunal* unless this notification is given within four weeks of notification of the *Adjudicator's* decision.

(3) If the *Adjudicator* does not notify his decision within the time provided by this contract, a Party may notify the other Party that he intends to refer the dispute to the *tribunal*. A Party may not refer a dispute to the *tribunal* unless this notification is given within four weeks of the date by which the *Adjudicator* should have notified his decision.

(4) The *tribunal* settles the dispute referred to it. The *tribunal* has the powers to reconsider any decision of the *Adjudicator* and review and revise any action or inaction of the *Employer* related to the dispute. A Party is not limited in the *tribunal* proceedings to the information, evidence or arguments put to the *Adjudicator*.

(5) If *tribunal* is arbitration, the *arbitration procedure*, the place where the arbitration is to be held and the method of choosing the arbitrator are those stated in the Contract Data.

(6) A Party does not call the *Adjudicator* as a witness in *tribunal* proceedings.

Option W2

Dispute resolution procedure (used in the United Kingdom when the Housing Grants, Construction and Regeneration Act 1996 applies).

Dispute resolution W2

W2.1 (1) Any dispute arising under or in connection with this contract is referred to and decided by the *Adjudicator*. A Party may refer a dispute to the *Adjudicator* at any time.

(2) In this Option, time periods stated in days exclude Christmas Day, Good Friday and bank holidays.

The *Adjudicator* W2.2 (1) The Parties appoint the *Adjudicator* under the NEC Adjudicator's Contract current at the *starting date*.

(2) The *Adjudicator* acts impartially and decides the dispute as an independent adjudicator and not as an arbitrator.

(3) If the *Adjudicator* is not identified in the Contract Data or if the *Adjudicator* resigns or becomes unable to act

- the Parties may choose an adjudicator jointly or
- a Party may ask the *Adjudicator nominating body* to choose an adjudicator.

The *Adjudicator nominating body* chooses an adjudicator within four days of the request. The chosen adjudicator becomes the *Adjudicator.*

(4) A replacement *Adjudicator* has the power to decide a dispute referred to his predecessor but not decided at the time when his predecessor resigned or became unable to act. He deals with an undecided dispute as if it had been referred to him on the date he was appointed.

(5) The *Adjudicator,* his employees and agents are not liable to the Parties for any action or failure to take action in an adjudication unless the action or failure to take action was in bad faith.

The adjudication W2.3 (1) Before a Party refers a dispute to the *Adjudicator*, he gives a notice of adjudication to the other Party with a brief description of the dispute and the decision which he wishes the *Adjudicator* to make. If the *Adjudicator* is named in the Contract Data, the Party sends a copy of the notice of adjudication to the *Adjudicator* when it is issued. Within three days of the receipt of the notice of adjudication, the *Adjudicator* notifies the Parties

- that he is able to decide the dispute in accordance with the contract or
- that he is unable to decide the dispute and has resigned.

If the *Adjudicator* does not so notify within three days of the issue of the notice of adjudication, either Party may act as if he has resigned.

(2) Within seven days of a Party giving a notice of adjudication he

- refers the dispute to the *Adjudicator*,
- provides the *Adjudicator* with the information on which he relies, including any supporting documents and
- provides a copy of the information and supporting documents he has provided to the *Adjudicator* to the other Party.

Any further information from a Party to be considered by the *Adjudicator* is provided within fourteen days from the referral. This period may be extended if the *Adjudicator* and Parties agree.

core clauses

main option clauses

secondary option clauses

contract data

core clauses

main option clauses

secondary option clauses

contract data

(3a) If a matter disputed by the *Consultant* under or in connection with a subcontract is also a matter disputed under or in connection with this contract, the *Consultant* may, with the consent of the Subconsultant, refer the subcontract dispute to the *Adjudicator* at the same time as the main contract referral. The *Adjudicator* then decides the disputes together and references to the Parties for the purposes of the dispute are interpreted as including the Subconsultant.

(3b) If this contract is a subcontract and the main contract provides for joint adjudication of disputes, the following procedure applies.

Within two weeks of the notification of the dispute by the *Consultant* to the *Employer*, the *Employer* notifies the *Consultant* if the matter disputed is a matter disputed under or in connection with the main contract.

The *Employer* may then

- submit the subcontract dispute to the main contract Adjudicator at the same time as the main contract submission and
- instruct the *Consultant* to provide any information which the *Employer* may require.

The main contract Adjudicator then gives his decision on the disputes together.

(4) The *Adjudicator* may

- review and revise any action or inaction of the *Employer* related to the dispute and after a quotation which has been treated as having been accepted,
- take the initiative in ascertaining the facts and the law related to the dispute,
- instruct a Party to provide further information related to the dispute within a stated time and
- instruct a Party to take any other action which he considers necessary to reach his decision and to do so within a stated time.

(5) If a Party does not comply with any instruction within the time stated by the *Adjudicator,* the *Adjudicator* may continue the adjudication and make his decision based upon the information and evidence he has received.

(6) A communication between a Party and the *Adjudicator* is communicated to the other Party at the same time.

(7) If the *Adjudicator's* decision includes assessment of additional cost or delay caused to the *Consultant,* he makes his assessment in the same way as a compensation event is assessed.

(8) The *Adjudicator* decides the dispute and notifies the Parties of his decision and his reasons within twenty-eight days of the dispute being referred to him. This period may be extended by up to fourteen days with the consent of the referring Party or by any other period agreed by the Parties.

(9) Unless and until the *Adjudicator* has notified the Parties of his decision, the Parties proceed as if the matter disputed was not disputed.

(10) If the *Adjudicator* does not make his decision and notify it to the Parties within the time provided by this contract the Parties and the *Adjudicator* may agree to extend the period for making his decision. If they do not agree to an extension, either Party may act as if the *Adjudicator* has resigned.

(11) The *Adjudicator's* decision is binding on the Parties unless and until revised by the *tribunal* and is enforceable as a matter of contractual obligation between the Parties and not as an arbitral award. The *Adjudicator's* decision is final and binding if neither Party has notified the other within the times required by this contract that he is dissatisfied with a matter decided by the *Adjudicator* and intends to refer the matter to the *tribunal*.

(12) The *Adjudicator* may, within fourteen days of giving his decision to the Parties, correct a clerical mistake or ambiguity.

Review by the *tribunal* W2.4 (1) A Party does not refer any dispute under or in connection with this contract to the *tribunal* unless it has first been decided by the *Adjudicator* in accordance with this contract.

(2) If, after the *Adjudicator* notifies his decision a Party is dissatisfied, that Party may notify the other Party of the matter which he disputes and state that he intends to refer it to the *tribunal*. The dispute may not be referred to the *tribunal* unless this notification is given within four weeks of the notification of the *Adjudicator's* decision.

(3) The *tribunal* settles the dispute referred to it. The *tribunal* has the powers to reconsider any decision of the *Adjudicator* and to review and revise any action or inaction of the *Employer* related to the dispute. A Party is not limited in *tribunal* proceedings to the information or evidence put to the *Adjudicator*.

(4) If the *tribunal* is arbitration, the *arbitration procedure*, the place where the arbitration is to be held and the method of choosing the arbitrator are those stated in the Contract Data.

(5) A Party does not call the *Adjudicator* as a witness in *tribunal* proceedings.

core clauses

main option clauses

secondary option clauses

contract data

Option X1: Price adjustment for inflation

If *staff rates* are fixed at the Contract Date and are not variable with changes in salary paid to individuals.

Price adjustment factor **X1**

X1.1   On each anniversary of the Contract Date, the *Consultant* calculates a price adjustment factor equal to $(L - B)/B$, where L is the last published value of the *index* and B is the last value of the *index* published before the Contract Date.

If an *index* is changed after it has been used in calculating a price adjustment factor, the calculation is repeated and a correction included in the next assessment of the amount due.

The price adjustment factor calculated at the Completion Date for the whole of the *services* is used for calculating price adjustment after this date.

Price adjustment X1.2   Each amount due after the first anniversary includes an amount for price adjustment which is the sum of

- the change in the Price for Services Provided to Date since the last assessment of the amount due multiplied by the price adjustment factor calculated at the last anniversary and
- the amount for price adjustment included in the previous amount due.

Price adjustment **Option C** X1.3   Each time the amount due is assessed after the first anniversary, an amount for price adjustment is added to the total of the Prices which is the change in the Price for Services Provided to Date since the last assessment of the amount due multiplied by $(PAF/(1+PAF))$ where PAF is the price adjustment factor calculated at the last anniversary.

***Expenses* adjustment** X1.6   If payment rates for any of the *expenses* are fixed at the Contract Date and are not otherwise adjustable for inflation, each amount due after the first anniversary includes an amount for *expenses* adjustment which is the sum of

- the change in fixed *expenses* since the last assessment of the amount due multiplied by the price adjustment factor calculated at the last anniversary and
- the amount for *expenses* adjustment included in the previous amount due.

If *staff rates* are variable with changes in salary paid to individuals.

Price adjustment factor **X1**

X1.1   On each anniversary of the Contract Date, the *Consultant* calculates a price adjustment factor equal to $(L-B)/B$, where L is the last published value of the *index* and B is the last value of the *index* published before the Contract Date.

If an *index* is changed after it has been used in calculating a price adjustment factor, the calculation is repeated and a correction included in the next assessment of the amount due.

The price adjustment factor calculated at the Completion Date for the whole of the *services* is used for calculating price adjustment after this date.

Price adjustment **Option A**	X1.2	Each amount due after the first anniversary includes an amount for price adjustment which is the sum of

- the change in the Price for Services Provided to Date since the last assessment of the amount due multiplied by the price adjustment factor calculated at the last anniversary and
- the amount for price adjustment included in the previous amount due.

Price adjustment **Option C**	X1.3	Each time the amount due is assessed after the first anniversary, an amount for price adjustment is added to the total of the Prices which is the change in the Price for Services Provided to Date since the last assessment of the amount due multiplied by $(PAF/(1+PAF))$ where PAF is the price adjustment factor calculated at the last anniversary.

Price adjustment **Option G**	X1.4	Each amount due after the first anniversary includes an amount for price adjustment which is the sum of

- for the lump sum items on the Task Schedule, the change in the lump sums included in the Price for Services Provided to Date since the last assessment of the amount due multiplied by the price adjustment factor calculated at the last anniversary before the assessment and
- the amount for price adjustment included in the previous amount due.

Compensation events **Options A, C and G** **(lump sum items on the** **Task Schedule) only**	X1.5	The Time Charge for compensation events is assessed using the *staff rates* current at the time of assessing the compensation event adjusted to the Contract Date by dividing by $(1+PAF)$, where PAF is the price adjustment factor calculated at the last anniversary.

***Expenses* adjustment**	X1.6	If payment rates for any of the *expenses* are fixed at the Contract Date and are not otherwise adjustable for inflation, each amount due after the first anniversary includes an amount for *expenses* adjustment which is the sum of

- the change in fixed *expenses* since the last assessment of the amount due multiplied by the price adjustment factor calculated at the last anniversary and
- the amount for *expenses* adjustment included in the previous amount due.

Option X2: Changes in the law

Changes in the law	**X2**	
	X2.1	A change in the *law of the project* is a compensation event if it occurs after the Contract Date. Either Party may notify the other of a compensation event for a change in the law. If the effect of a compensation event which is a change in the law is to reduce the total Time Charge, the Prices are reduced.

Option X3: Multiple currencies (used only with Options A and G)

Multiple currencies	**X3**	
	X3.1	The *Consultant* is paid in currencies other than the *currency of this contract* for the items or activities listed in the Contract Data. The *exchange rates* are used to convert from the *currency of this contract* to other currencies.

core clauses

main option clauses

secondary option clauses

contract data

X3.2 Payments to the *Consultant* in currencies other than the *currency of this contract* do not exceed the maximum amounts stated in the Contract Data. Any excess is paid in the *currency of this contract*.

Option X4: Parent company guarantee

Parent company **X4**
guarantee X4.1 If a parent company owns the *Consultant*, the *Consultant* gives to the *Employer* a guarantee by the *Consultant*'s parent company of the *Consultant*'s performance in the form set out in the Scope. If the guarantee was not given by the Contract Date, it is given to the *Employer* within four weeks of the Contract Date.

Option X5: Sectional Completion (not used with Option G)

Sectional Completion **X5**
X5.1 In these *conditions of contract*, unless stated as the whole of the *services*, each reference and clause relevant to

- the *services*,
- Completion and
- Completion Date

applies, as the case may be, to either the whole of the *services* or any *section* of the *services*.

Option X6: Bonus for early Completion (not used with Option G)

Bonus for early Completion **X6**
X6.1 The *Consultant* is paid a bonus calculated at the rate stated in the Contract Data for each day from Completion until the Completion Date.

Option X7: Delay damages

Delay damages **X7**
Options A, C and E X7.1 The *Consultant* pays delay damages at the rate stated in the Contract Data for each day from the Completion Date until Completion.

X7.2 If the Completion Date is changed to a later date after delay damages have been paid, the *Employer* repays the overpayment of damages with interest. Interest is assessed from the date of payment to the date of repayment and the date of repayment is an assessment date.

(side tabs:) core clauses | main option clauses | secondary option clauses | contract data

Option G only	X7.3	The *Consultant* pays delay damages at the rate stated in the Task Order for each day from the Task Completion Date until Task Completion.
	X7.4	If the Task Completion Date is changed to a later date after delay damages have been paid, the *Employer* repays the overpayment of delay damages with interest. Interest is assessed from the date of payment to the date of repayment and the date of repayment is an assessment date.

Option X8: *Collateral warranty agreements*

Collateral warranty agreements	**X8**	
	X8.1	The *Consultant* enters into the *collateral warranty agreements*.

Option X9: Transfer of rights

Transfer of rights	**X9**	
	X9.1	The *Employer* owns the *Consultant*'s rights over material prepared for this contract by the *Consultant* except as stated otherwise in the Scope. The *Consultant* obtains other rights for the *Employer* as stated in the Scope and obtains from a Subconsultant equivalent rights for the *Employer* over the material prepared by the Subconsultant. The *Consultant* provides to the *Employer* the documents which transfer these rights to the *Employer*.

Option X10: *Employer's Agent*

Employer's Agent	**X10**	
	X10.1	The *Employer's Agent* acts on behalf of the *Employer* with the authority set out in the Contract Data.
	X10.2	The *Employer* may replace the *Employer's Agent* after he has notified the *Consultant* of the name of the replacement.

Option X11: Termination by the *Employer*

Termination by the *Employer*	**X11**	
	X11.1	The *Employer* may terminate the *Consultant*'s obligation to Provide the Services for a reason not stated in this contract by notifying the *Consultant*.

core clauses

main option clauses

secondary option clauses

contract data

X11.2 If the *Employer* terminates for a reason not stated in this contract, an additional amount is due on termination which is 5% of the difference between

- the forecast of the final total of the Prices in the absence of termination and
- the total of the other amounts and costs included in the amount due on termination.

Option X12: Partnering

Identified and defined terms **X12**

X12.1 (1) The Partners are those named in the Schedule of Partners. The *Client* is a Partner.

(2) An Own Contract is a contract between two Partners which includes this Option.

(3) The Core Group comprises the Partners listed in the Schedule of Core Group Members.

(4) Partnering Information is information which specifies how the Partners work together and is either in the documents which the Contract Data states it is in or in an instruction given in accordance with this contact.

(5) A Key Performance Indicator is an aspect of performance for which a target is stated in the Schedule of Partners.

Actions X12.2 (1) Each Partner works with other Partners to achieve the *Client's objective* stated in the Contract Data and the objectives of every other Partner stated in the Schedule of Partners.

(2) Each Partner nominates a representative to act for him in dealings with other Partners.

(3) The Core Group acts and takes decisions on behalf of the Partners on those matters stated in the Partnering Information.

(4) The Partners select the members of the Core Group. The Core Group decides how they will work and decides the dates when each member joins and leaves the Core Group. The *Client*'s representative leads the Core Group unless stated otherwise in the Partnering Information.

(5) The Core Group keeps the Schedule of Core Group Members and the Schedule of Partners up to date and issues copies of them to the Partners each time either is revised.

(6) This Option does not create a legal partnership between Partners who are not one of the Parties in this contract.

Working together X12.3 (1) The Partners work together as stated in the Partnering Information and in a spirit of mutual trust and co-operation.

(2) A Partner may ask another Partner to provide information which he needs to carry out the work in his Own Contract and the other Partner provides it.

(3) Each Partner gives an early warning to the other Partners when he becomes aware of any matter that could affect the achievement of another Partner's objectives stated in the Schedule of Partners.

(4) The Partners use common information systems as set out in the Partnering Information.

core clauses

main option clauses

secondary option clauses

contract data

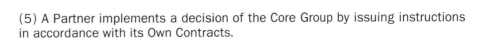
(5) A Partner implements a decision of the Core Group by issuing instructions in accordance with its Own Contracts.

(6) The Core Group may give an instruction to the Partners to change the Partnering Information. Each such change to the Partnering Information is a compensation event which may lead to reduced Prices.

(7) The Core Group prepares and maintains a timetable showing the proposed timing of the contributions of the Partners. The Core Group issues a copy of the timetable to the Partners each time it is revised. The *Consultant* changes his programme if it is necessary to do so in order to comply with the revised timetable. Each such change is a compensation event which may lead to reduced Prices.

(8) A Partner gives advice, information and opinion to the Core Group and to other Partners when asked to do so by the Core Group. This advice, information and opinion relates to work that another Partner is to carry out under its Own Contract and is given fully, openly and objectively. The Partners show contingency and risk allowances in information about costs, prices and timing for future work.

(9) A Partner notifies the Core Group before subcontracting any work.

Incentives X12.4 (1) A Partner is paid the amount stated in the Schedule of Partners if the target stated for a Key Performance Indicator is improved upon or achieved. Payment of the amount is due when the target has been improved upon or achieved and is made as part of the amount due in the Partner's Own Contract.

(2) The *Client* may add a Key Performance Indicator and associated payment to the Schedule of Partners but may not delete or reduce a payment stated in the Schedule of Partners.

Option X13: Performance bond

Performance bond **X13**

X13.1 The *Consultant* gives the *Employer* a performance bond, provided by a bank or insurer which the *Employer* has accepted, for the amount stated in the Contract Data and in the form set out in the Scope. A reason for not accepting the bank or insurer is that its commercial position is not strong enough to carry the bond. If the bond was not given by the Contract Date, it is given to the *Employer* within four weeks of the Contract Date.

Option X18: Limitation of liability

Limitation of liability **X18**

X18.1 The *Consultant*'s liability to the *Employer* for the *Employer*'s indirect or consequential loss is limited to the amount stated in the Contract Data.

X18.2 The *Consultant*'s liability to the *Employer* for Defects that are not found until after the *defects date* is limited to the amount stated in the Contract Data.

X18.3 The *Consultant* is not liable to the *Employer* for a matter unless it is notified to the *Consultant* before the *end of liability date*.

core clauses

main option clauses

secondary option clauses

contract data

Option X20: Key Performance Indicators (not used with Option X12)

Incentives **X20**

X20.1 A Key Performance Indicator is an aspect of performance by the *Consultant* for which a target is stated in the Incentive Schedule. The Incentive Schedule is the *incentive schedule* unless later changed in accordance with this contract.

X20.2 From the *starting date* until the *defects date*, the *Consultant* reports to the *Employer* his performance against each of the Key Performance Indicators. Reports are provided at the intervals stated in the Contract Data and include the forecast final measurement against each indicator.

X20.3 If the *Consultant*'s forecast final measurement against a Key Performance Indicator will not achieve the target stated in the Incentive Schedule, he submits his proposals for improving performance.

X20.4 The *Consultant* is paid the amount stated in the Incentive Schedule if the target stated for a Key Performance Indicator is improved upon or achieved. Payment of the amount is due when the target has been improved upon or achieved.

X20.5 The *Employer* may add a Key Performance Indicator and associated payment to the Incentive Schedule but may not delete or reduce a payment stated in the Incentive Schedule.

core clauses

main option clauses

secondary option clauses

contract data

Option Y

Option Y(UK)2: The Housing Grants, Construction and Regeneration Act 1996

Definitions **Y(UK)2**

Y2.1 (1) The Act is the Housing Grants, Construction and Regeneration Act 1996.

(2) A period of time stated in days is a period calculated in accordance with Section 116 of the Act.

Dates for payment Y2.2 The date on which a payment becomes due is seven days after the date of the *Consultant*'s invoice.

The final date for payment is fourteen days or a different period for payment if stated in the Contract Data after the date on which payment becomes due.

Not later than five days after the date on which a payment becomes due, the *Employer* issues a notice to the *Consultant* stating the amount of payment made or proposed to be made, and the basis on which the amount was calculated.

Notice of intention to withhold payment Y2.3 If either Party intends to withhold payment of an amount due under this contract, he notifies the other Party not later than seven days (the prescribed period) before the final date for payment by stating the amount proposed to be withheld and the reason for withholding payment. If there is more than one reason, the amount for each reason is stated.

A Party does not withhold payment of an amount due under this contract unless he has notified his intention to withhold payment as required by this contract.

Suspension of performance Y2.4 If the *Consultant* exercises his right under the Act to suspend performance, it is a compensation event.

Option Y(UK)3: The Contracts (Rights of Third Parties) Act 1999

Third party rights **Y(UK)3**

Y3.1 A person or organisation who is not one of the Parties may enforce a term of this contract under the Contracts (Rights of Third Parties) Act 1999 only if the term and the person or organisation are stated in the Contract Data.

Option Z: *Additional conditions of contract*

Additional conditions of contract **Z1.1** The *additional conditions of contract* stated in the Contract Data are part of this contract.

CONTRACT DATA

Part one – Data provided by the *Employer*

Completion of the data in full, according to the Options chosen, is essential to create a complete contract.

Statements given in all contracts

1 General

- The *conditions of contract* are the core clauses and the clauses for main Option ....., dispute resolution Option ..... and secondary Options ..... of the NEC3 Professional Services Contract June 2005 (with amendments June 2006).
- The *Employer* is

  Name ....

  Address ....

  ....

- The *Adjudicator* is

  Name ....

  Address ....

  ....

- The *services* are

  ....

  ....

- The Scope is in

  ....

  ....

- The *language of this contract* is ....
- The *law of the contract* is the law of ....
- The *period for reply* is .... weeks.
- The *period for retention* is .... years following Completion or earlier termination.
- The *Adjudicator nominating body* is ....
- The *tribunal* is ....
- The following matters will be included in the Risk Register

  ....

  ....

2 The Parties' main responsibilities

- The *Employer* provides access to the following persons, places and things

access to   *access date*

....

....

....

....

3 Time

- The *starting date* is . . . .
- The *Consultant* submits revised programmes at intervals no longer than . . . . . weeks.

4 Quality

- The quality policy statement and quality plan are provided within . . . . weeks of the Contract Date.
- The *defects date* is . . . . weeks after Completion of the whole of the *services.*

5 Payment

- The *assessment interval* is . . . .
- The *currency of this contract* is . . . .
- The *interest rate* is . . . . . .% per annum (not less than 2) above the . . . . rate of the . . . . bank.

8 Indemnity, insurance and liability

- The amounts of insurance and the periods for which the *Consultant* maintains insurance are

event	cover	period following Completion of the whole of the *services* or earlier termination
failure of the *Consultant* to use the skill and care normally used by professionals providing services similar to the *services*	. . . . in respect of each claim, without limit to the number of claims	. . . .
death of or bodily injury to a person (not an employee of the *Consultant*) or loss of or damage to property resulting from an action or failure to take action by the *Consultant*	. . . . in respect of each claim, without limit to the number of claims	. . . .
death of or bodily injury to employees of the *Consultant* arising out of and in the course of their employment in connection with this contract	. . . . in respect of each claim, without limit to the number of claims	. . . .

core clauses

main option clauses

secondary option clauses

contract data

- The *Employer* provides the following insurances

. . . .

. . . .

. . . .

- The *Consultant*'s total liability to the *Employer* for all matters arising under or in connection with this contract, other than the excluded matters, is limited to

. . . .

Optional statements

If the *Employer* has decided the *completion date* for the whole of the *services*

- The *completion date* for the whole of the *services* is . . . .

If no programme is identified in part two of the Contract Data

- The *Consultant* is to submit a first programme for acceptance within. . . . . weeks of the Contract Date.

If the *Employer* has identified work which is to meet a stated *condition* by a *key date*

- The *key dates* and *conditions* to be met are

condition to be met	*key date*
1	. . . .
2	. . . .
3	. . . .

If the period in which payments are made is not three weeks and Y(UK)2 is not used

- The period within which payments are made is . . . .

If Y(UK)2 is used and the final date for payment is not 14 days after the date when payment is due

- The period for payment is . . . .

If the *Employer* states any *expenses*

- The *expenses* stated by the *Employer* are

item	amount
. . . .	. . . .
. . . .	. . . .
. . . .	. . . .

If the *Consultant* is to provide additional insurances

- The *Consultant* provides these additional insurances

1. Insurance against. . . . .

Cover is . . . .

Period of cover. . . . .

Deductibles are. . . . .

2. Insurance against. . . . .

Cover is . . . .

Period of cover. . . . .

Deductibles are. . . . .

If the *tribunal* is arbitration

- The *arbitration procedure* is

  . . . .

- The place where arbitration is to be held is

  . . . .

- The person or organisation who will choose an arbitrator
  - if the Parties cannot agree a choice or
  - if the *arbitration procedure* does not state who selects an arbitrator is

  . . . .

If this contract is a subcontract and the main contract provides for joint adjudication of disputes

- The main contract Adjudicator is . . . .

If Option A is used

- The *Consultant* prepares forecasts of the total *expenses* at intervals no longer than . . . . weeks.

If Option C, E or G is used

- The *Consultant* prepares forecasts of the total Time Charge and *expenses* at intervals no longer than . . . . weeks.

- The *exchange rates* are those published in . . . . on . . . . (date).

If Option C is used

- The *Consultant's share percentages* and the *share ranges* are

share range		*Consultant's share percentage*	
less than	%	. . . .	%
from . . . . % to	%	. . . .	%
from . . . . % to	%	. . . .	%
greater than	%	. . . .	%

If Option X1 is used

- The *index* is . . . .

If Option X2 is used

- The *law of the project* is . . . .

  . . . .

  . . . .

core clauses

main option clauses

secondary option clauses

contract data

core clauses

main option clauses

secondary option clauses

contract data

If Option X3 is used

- The *Employer* will pay for the items or activities listed below in the currencies stated

items and activities	other currency	total maximum payment in the currency
1	....	....
2	....	....
3	....	....

- The *exchange rates* are those published in ....

  on .... (date)

If Option X5 is used

- The *completion date* for each *section* of the *services* is

section	description	completion date
1	....	....
2	....	....
3	....	....
4	....	....
5	....	....

If Options X5 and X6 are used together

- The bonuses for each *section* of the *services* are

section	description	amount per day
1	....	....
2	....	....
3	....	....
4	....	....
5	....	....

Remainder of the *services*. ....

If Options X5 and X7 are used together

- Delay damages for each *section* of the *services* are

section	description	amount per day
1	....	....
2	....	....
3	....	....
4	....	....
5	....	....

Remainder of the *services*. ....

If Option X6 is used (but not if Option X5 is also used)

- The bonus for the whole of the *services* is . . . . per day.

If Option X7 is used (whether or not Option X5 is also used; used only with main Options A, C and E)

- Delay damages for Completion of the whole of the *services* are . . . . per day.

If Option X8 is used

- The *collateral warranty agreements* are

agreement reference	third party
. . . .	. . . .
. . . .	. . . .
. . . .	. . . .
. . . .	. . . .

If Option X10 is used

- The *Employer's Agent* is

  Name . . . .

  Address . . . .

  . . . .

  . . . .

- The authority of the *Employer's Agent* is

  . . . .

If Option X12 is used

- The *Client* is

  Name . . . .

  Address . . . .

  . . . .

- The *Client's objective* is . . . .

  . . . .

  . . . .

  . . . .

  . . . .

  . . . .

- The Partnering Information is in . . . .

  . . . .

  . . . .

  . . . .

  . . . .

  . . . .

core clauses

main option clauses

secondary option clauses

contract data

If Option X13 is used

- The amount of the performance bond is . . . .

If Option X18 is used

- The *Consultant*'s liability to the *Employer* for indirect or consequential loss is limited to . . . .

- The *Consultant*'s liability to the *Employer* for Defects that are not found until after the *defects date* is limited to . . . .

- The *end of liability date* is . . . . years after Completion of the whole of the *services*.

If Option X20 is used (but not if Option X12 is also used)

- The *incentive schedule* for Key Performance Indicators is in . . . .

- A report of performance against each Key Performance Indicator is provided at intervals of . . . . months

If Option Y(UK)3 is used

- term   person or organisation

  . . . .

  . . . .

  . . . .

  . . . .

If Option Z is used

- The *additional conditions of contract* are . . . .

  . . . .

core clauses

main option clauses

secondary option clauses

contract data

Part two – Data provided by the *Consultant*

Completion of the data in full, according to the Options chosen, is essential to create a complete contract.

Statements given in all contracts

- The *Consultant* is. . . . .

  Name . . . .

  Address . . . .

  . . . .

  . . . .

- The *key persons* are

  (1) Name . . . .

  Job . . . .

  Responsibilities. . . . .

  Qualifications. . . . .

  Experience. . . . .

  (2) Name . . . .

  Job . . . .

  Responsibilities. . . . .

  Qualifications. . . . .

  Experience. . . . .

- The *staff rates* are

  name/designation   rate

  . . . .

  . . . .

- The following matters will be included in the Risk Register

  . . . .

  . . . .

  . . . .

  . . . .

Optional statements

If the *Consultant* is to decide the *completion date* for the whole of the *services*

- The *completion date* for the whole of the *services* is . . . .

If a programme is to be identified in the Contract Data

- The programme identified in the Contract Data is . . . .

If the *Consultant* states any *expenses*

- The *expenses* stated by the *Consultant* are

  item   amount

  . . . .

  . . . .

core clauses

main option clauses

secondary option clauses

contract data

© copyright nec 2005

If the *Consultant* requires additional access

• The *Employer* provides access to the following persons, places and things

access to   *access date*

. . . .

. . . .

If Option A or C is used

• The *activity schedule* is . . . .

• The tendered total of the Prices is . . . .

If Option G is used

• The *task schedule* is . . . .

nec®3 Professional Services Contract

Index by clause numbers (Option clauses indicated by their letters, main clause heads by bold numbers). Terms in *italics* are identified in Contract Data, and defined terms have capital initial letters.
